# Goosebumps

## OFFICIAL COLLECTOR'S CAPS BOOK

## R.L. STINE

AN
**APPLE**
PAPERBACK

D1502475

SCHOLASTIC INC.
New York  Toronto  London  Auckland  Sydney

A PARACHUTE PRESS BOOK

ISBN 0-590-60617-4

12 11 10 9 8 7 6 5 4                    5 6 7 8 9/9 0/0

Printed in the U.S.A.                    40

First Scholastic printing, June 1995

## Collector's Slammer
## Curly — #1 GOOSEBUMPS Fan

Boo, Dude! Curly here to welcome you to the *Goosebumps Collector's Caps Collecting Kit.* It's got sixteen of the coolest collector's caps around.

But first check out the slammer. That's me. And make no bones about it. I'm the *coolest* slammer around! You can use me in the super *Goosebumps* Cap Slappin' Game you'll find on page 36 in your Collector's Kit book — a totally awesome book.

Totally awesome. Because it's got information that *Goosebumps* fans have to know — and can't find anyplace else!

First you'll read **The Story** behind each *Goosebumps* cap. Keep going. Because **The Story Behind the Story** comes next — and you won't want to miss that — or any of the **Frightening Facts**, **Top Secrets! For *Goosebumps* Fans Only!**, **Totally Awesome** moments, or jokes we've thrown in to **Have a Good Shriek!** The pages are filled with inside information about your favorite *Goosebumps* books and secrets about R.L. Stine you never knew!

Then move on to our **Petrifying Puzzles and Gruesome Games** — only if you have the *guts* to do them. I don't!

Have a totally excellent time with your *Goosebumps Collector's Caps Collecting Kit*, dude. And have a scary day!

**Collector's Cap #*1***
**The Masked Mutant — He's a Super Villain!**
**from**
**ATTACK OF THE MUTANT**

*Goosebumps* #**25**

**Published November 1994**

**THE STORY:** Skipper Matthews collects comics. His favorite one is about The Masked Mutant, an evil super villain who wants to rule the universe. Then one day Skipper loses his way in a strange part of town, where he and his new friend, Libby, discover The Mutant's secret headquarters! Does The Masked Mutant really live in Riverview Falls?

**THE STORY BEHIND THE STORY:** Skipper really loves comics, but do you think he'd give up the hair on his head to read them? R.L. Stine did.

When R.L. was a kid, he loved to read spooky comics called *Tales from the Crypt* and *Vault of Horror*. Unfortunately, his mother did not let him buy them or read them in their house. The only place R.L. could read his favorite comics was at the barbershop, where they always had the latest issues. So R.L. got a haircut every week!

**TOP SECRET! FOR GOOSEBUMPS FANS ONLY!:** In *Attack of the Mutant*, The Masked Mutant's foes are called The League of Good Guys. There are six superheroes in the league. Skipper mentions only three of them: The Amazing Tornado-man, The Galloping Gazelle, and SpongeLife (The Sponge of Steel). The other three members are: Rott Weiler— The Human Guard Dog, Clara the Claw Woman (she has nine-inch nails), and The Fantastic Ferret (the underground superhero).

**TOTALLY AWESOME! The parts of the book you'll never forget:** Remember when Skipper thought Libby melted The Masked Mutant — but she didn't? You don't remember? To find out who she did melt, go around the circle clockwise writing down every other letter. You'll get the answer!

Answer on Page 47.

**Collector's Cap #2**
**The Mummy Lives!**
**from**
**THE CURSE OF THE**
**MUMMY'S TOMB**

### Goosebumps #5

**Published January 1993**

**THE STORY:** Exploring an ancient pyramid in Egypt with Uncle Ben will be totally awesome! That's what Gabe thinks when he visits his uncle and his cousin Sari. Then Gabe finds himself deep inside the pyramid. Alone. And trapped! Gabe says he doesn't believe in the curse of the mummy's tomb. Maybe now he's changed his mind!

**THE STORY BEHIND THE STORY:** Remember all the disgusting facts that Gabe tells Sari about mummies? Who could forget the one about the ancient Egyptians using a tool to pull the dead person's brain out through his nose! All the facts are true. And Gabe knows a lot more creepy stuff about mummies. Here are some frightening facts he wants *you* to know:

• Sometimes, in ancient Egypt, if a mummy was too tall for his coffin, someone would break his legs to make him fit!

• Before a body was mummified, all the internal organs—like the stomach, liver, and lungs — were removed, except for the heart. Ancient Egyptians left the heart in the body because they believed it was the center of all feelings.

• A hundred years ago, everyone was wild about mummies. So wild, in fact, that they held mummy unwrapping parties. And they used real mummies!

**HAVE A GOOD SHRIEK!:** Gabe's uncle Ben loves to tell mummy jokes. Here's a riddle he told to Gabe and Sari. You'll have to use the code to unravel the answer to this one!

Why didn't the mummy have any hobbies?
Answer: *@ #+! +>> ($@: %/ $? *$! #<)"

**CODE:**
H=* W=# L=> N=? K=" I=$ E=@ O=<
T=( D=: A=+ S=! U=% R=) P=/

Answer on page 47.

**Collector's Cap #3**
**Evan Ross — Big Man on Campus!**
**from**
**MONSTER BLOOD III**

# Goosebumps #29

**Published March 1995**

**THE STORY:** Evan can't stand baby-sitting his genius cousin Kermit. Kermit is always playing practical jokes on Evan and his friend Andy. But now they have the perfect way to even up the score with Kermit— Monster Blood! But the joke's on Evan when things go more than a little wrong. And Evan starts growing bigger . . . and . . . bigger . . . and bigger . . . !

**THE STORY BEHIND THE STORY:** *Goosebumps* fans have been wondering just how big Monster Blood can make things grow. Now you can figure it out!

In *Monster Blood III*, Evan started as five feet tall, and after only eating a little bit of Monster Blood, he grew to twenty feet tall. That's four times larger. So if you fed the same amount of Monster Blood to a ten-feet-tall elephant, it would grow to approximately forty feet tall!

**FRIGHTENING FACTS:** It may be a coincidence, but *Monster Blood III* has a cast of characters with real superstar names. Check it out — there's Conan the Barbarian, Trigger (Roy Roger's horse), and Kermit (unfortunately, he's no frog!).

**Collector's Cap #4**
**The Mask — a Halloween Horror!**
**from**
**THE HAUNTED MASK**

**Goosebumps** #11

**Published September 1993**

**THE STORY:** Carly Beth has the scariest Halloween mask around. In fact, it's the ugliest, most terrifying mask any kid has ever seen. The day goes by, and Halloween slowly comes to an end for everyone. Everyone except Carly. That's when she discovers how terrifying her mask really is! It won't come off!

**THE STORY BEHIND THE STORY:** Every *Goosebumps* fan knows the story of Carly Beth's mask, but here's a story you've never heard.

Once, long before Carly Beth moved into her neighborhood, a handsome teenager lived on Carly Beth's street. He was a good student, but he was failing chemistry. His chemistry teacher was very mean. He refused to spend any extra time helping the boy.

The boy took matters into his own hands. He crept into the chemistry lab late at night to practice a few experiments of his own. That's when it happened. He accidentally mixed the wrong chemicals in his test tube. The tube exploded all over him. But instead of burning his face, the chemicals aged him. He became an old man overnight! An old man with a thin mustache and a pinched face. He was desperate to get his old — or, rather, his young — face back. So he started experimenting with making masks — masks that came alive! You guessed it. He's the shopkeeper in *The Haunted Mask*. And the one who created the mask that Carly Beth bought!

**FRIGHTENING FACTS:** One Halloween, R.L. Stine's son, Matt, slipped on a creepy Halloween mask. When Matt tugged at the mask to take it off, it wouldn't budge. When R.L. saw this, he jumped right on the case — he ran to the computer and started writing *The Haunted Mask*! (Oh, if you were wondering, Matt did eventually manage to pull the mask off — by himself!)

**Collector's Cap #5**
**The Mud Monsters — They're Coming for You!**
**from**
**YOU CAN'T SCARE ME!**

# Goosebumps #15

## Published January 1994

**THE STORY:** Nothing scares Courtney. Nothing. Now that would be okay — if Courtney weren't such a big show-off. But she likes making Eddie and his friends look like frightened wimps. Well, Eddie's had enough. It's time to scare Courtney — no matter what. So Eddie convinces Courtney to come out to Muddy Creek. Where the Mud Monsters live. Who believes in Mud Monsters? Only Courtney does. But maybe Eddie should, too!

**THE STORY BEHIND THE STORY:** According to the Muddy Creek legend, the Mud Monsters come out of their muddy graves once a year to seek their revenge on the townspeople. But there are rumors that the Mud Monsters were spotted one other time.

A few years after the Mud Monsters sank into their muddy graves, a land developer decided to dig up Muddy Creek. He wanted to turn it into a water park. But as soon as the digging began, horrible accidents erupted at the work site. The workers and their machinery were sucked into the mud — never to be seen again. Only one worker survived. He told a terrifying tale. He said the workers were pulled under the mud by the Mud Monsters. And there, they became Mud Monsters themselves. Of course, no one believed him. Do you?

**TOP SECRET! FOR GOOSEBUMPS FANS ONLY!:** Nothing scares Courtney. But what *Goosebumps* fans want to know is: Does anything scare R.L. Stine? Secret sources say that R.L. is not afraid of the dark, or bugs, or snakes, or heights, or monsters. But there is one fear he can't conquer. He's afraid of deep water! With his spooky imagination, R.L. always thinks about the creepy things that could be lurking under the water. Things you can't see, until they . . . GRAB you!

**TOTALLY AWESOME! The parts of the book you'll never forget**: Remember the spooky words Eddie's teacher, Mr. Melvin, told the class about monsters? Unscramble the sentence, and you'll see them!

dream real scary The we as as up
can isn't the monsters world.

Answer on page 47.

**Collector's Cap #6**
**The Haunted Scarecrow**
**from**
**THE SCARECROW WALKS AT MIDNIGHT**

# Goosebumps #20

**Published May 1994**

**THE STORY:** Jodie and her brother, Mark, are visiting their grandparents' farm. But this summer, everything on the farm seems different. Only Stanley, the farmhand, is the same — he's as weird as ever. But Grandma and Grandpa are quieter than usual. Much quieter. And their single scarecrow out in the cornfield is gone. In its place loom twelve evil-looking ones. And at midnight they . . . come alive!

**THE STORY BEHIND THE STORY:** *The Scarecrow Walks at Midnight* was inspired by a true experience. Once R.L. Stine walked near a cornfield and saw a scarecrow *move*! At the time he thought the wind was blowing it. But now he's not so sure.

**FRIGHTENING FACTS:** Stanley brings the scarecrow to life with his book of ancient superstitions. Want to take a peek at some other creepy superstitions listed in Stanley's book? Check these out:

• If a child likes hitting people, after the child is dead and buried his or her hand will stick up out of the ground — and dogs will use it like a fire hydrant!

• If a fly falls into your drink, it means good luck.

• Eating a roasted mouse will cure whooping cough.

**TOTALLY AWESOME! The parts of the book you'll never forget:** According to Jodie, her brother Mark's vocabulary consists of only three words. And after reading *The Scarecrow Walks at Midnight*, you probably agree! Do you remember the three words? If you can't, we've given them to you below. But you'll have to unscramble them!

SRGOS; EDRIW; OLOC.

Answer on page 47.

**Collector's Cap #7**
**The Human Bee-ing**
**from**
**WHY I'M AFRAID OF BEES**

**Goosebumps #17**

**Published March 1994**

**THE STORY:**  Everybody makes fun of Gary Lutz. Everybody.  Gary doesn't have a single friend — but he does have a dream. More than anything in the world, Gary wants to be somebody else. Well, Gary's dream is about to come true.  Gary is about to get a new body. But not the one he had in mind — because this body has six legs and wings and stings!

**THE STORY BEHIND THE STORY:**  Remember what a brat Gary's little sister, Krissy, was in *Why I'm Afraid of Bees*?  Well, the rumor is that when Gary went to make his body-switching plans, he tried to set up a match for Krissy. Unfortunately, after running her profile through the computer several times, the people at Person-to-Person Vacations came to the conclusion that nobody wanted to be Krissy — not even for a week! True?  Could be.

**FRIGHTENING FACTS:**  Did you notice all the bugs that bug Gary? You didn't?  Well, Gary wasn't the only bug mentioned in this book.  Besides the hundreds and hundreds of bees that have room and board at Mr. Andretti's, there's . . .

• Gary's favorite video game, EcoScare '95. It's all about fighting poisonous ants.

• A dragonfly that tries to kill off Gary the bee.

• Person-to-Person Vacations. It's located on Roach Street!

**TOP SECRET! FOR GOOSEBUMPS FANS ONLY!:** Gary's a pretty allergic kid. Do you know what happens to him whenever he eats honey? Go around the circle clockwise, starting at the arrow. Write down every other letter, and you'll find the answer.

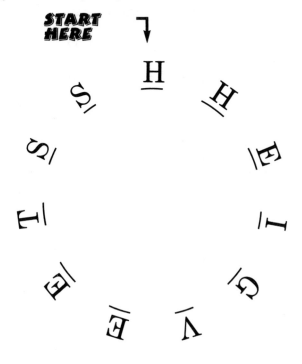

Answer on page 47.

**Collector's Cap #8**
**It's Green, It's Leafy, It's Dad!**
**from**
**STAY OUT OF THE BASEMENT**

# Goosebumps #2

**Published July 1992**

**THE STORY:** Margaret and Casey Brewer are really worried about their dad, Dr. Brewer. He's a scientist. And he's experimenting with some new kind of plant in the basement. What's the big deal about growing plants? Nothing, really. Until Margaret and Casey spy little green leaves sprouting from their dad's head!

**THE STORY BEHIND THE STORY:** *Stay Out of the Basement* was inspired by an old TV show where kids grew strange plants in their basement. In that story, though, the plants were mushrooms — mushrooms from outer space that wanted to rule the world! And you thought Margaret had it tough!

**HAVE A GOOD SHRIEK!:** If Dr. Brewer doesn't stop sprouting leaves on his head, what will Margaret and Casey do?
To find out, unscramble the letters below.

EAKM EIKL A ERET DAN EVALE!

Answer on page 47.

Collector's Cap #**9**
**Mr. Mortman—the Monster in the Library!**
**from**
**THE GIRL WHO CRIED MONSTER**

**Goosebumps** #**8**

**Published May 1993**

**THE STORY:** Lucy Dark loves to tell monster stories. She makes them up, of course. She has an incredible imagination. One day, Lucy discovers a real live monster — the summer school librarian! But no one will believe her. And that's too bad. Because this monster has a frightful plan. A plan to get Lucy!

**THE STORY BEHIND THE STORY:** As you know from reading *The Girl Who Cried Monster*, the Darks are not your average family. They look normal, and they do normal things, but they have a big secret. Which leads to a big question: Where do the Darks come from?

The Dark family is originally from Romania. They were forced to leave their native land because the country was swarming with monsters. So they sailed to America. They settled in Timberland Falls because they heard it was definitely monster-free. And the neighbors weren't nosy. It was just what the Darks needed. A safe place to bring up kids! And a safe place to keep their big secret — until the summer librarian came to town!

R.L. Stine named this book after an Aesop's fable called "The Boy Who Cried Wolf." In that story, a shepherd boy thought it would be fun to run into town yelling that a wolf was attacking the town's flock of sheep. The villagers were very angry when they hurried to help him and saw no wolf. Well, one day a wolf did attack, and the shepherd yelled (or cried) "Wolf" again. But no one believed him. No one ran to help him. And the wolf had all the lamb chops he could eat!

Because Lucy Dark always told monster stories, no one believed her, either, when she cried "Monster" for real!

**TOTALLY AWESOME! The parts of the book you'll never forget:** Most *Goosebumps* have a surprise ending, but *Goosebumps* fans will agree that the dinner scene at the end of *The Girl Who Cried Monster* is one of the best and biggest shockers of all! Some fans say the ending of *Attack of the Mutant* is a bigger surprise. What do you think?

**Collector's Cap #10**
**Wolf—Man's Best Friend**
**from**
**THE WEREWOLF OF FEVER SWAMP**

**Goosebumps #14**

**Published December 1993**

**THE STORY:** Something creepy lives in Fever Swamp. Something that howls at night. Something that kills small animals. Everyone thinks it's Grady's dog, Wolf. But Wolf is a nice dog, Grady thinks. Until he spies Wolf howling at the moon — and mysteriously disappearing at midnight!

**THE STORY BEHIND THE STORY:** Sometimes a single picture will inspire a *Goosebumps* book. Once when R.L. Stine was visiting Florida, he took a short boat ride through a swampy area. He was amazed to see a deer standing right in the middle of the swampy water. That deer stayed in his head — until it appeared in the pages of *Fever Swamp*!

**FRIGHTENING FACTS:** How did the werewolf of Fever Swamp become a werewolf? According to ancient legends, there are several ways to become a werewolf. If you are bitten by a werewolf, you're doomed to become one. If you eat meat killed by a wolf, you will turn into a wolfman. If you drink water from a wolf's footprint, you'll change into a werewolf.

Some werewolves become werewolves on purpose. They rub themselves with ointments made from ingredients such as bat's blood, or foxglove, wolfbane, and other strange plants. The werewolf of Fever Swamp accidentally started his life as a werewolf with ointments. He was just experimenting — unfortunately, the results were very hairy.

**HAVE A GOOD SHRIEK!:** Everyone knows this werewolf joke—that's why we've hidden the punchline. Cross out the letters S, W, A, M, P. Then unscramble the letters that are left, and you'll find the answer to the joke.

What do you call someone who puts his right arm down a werewolf's throat?

A S Y W A M F P E A A W L P P T

Answer on page 47.

**Collector's Cap #11**
**Hand Me a Scare**
**from**
**PIANO LESSONS CAN BE MURDER**

**Goosebumps #13**

**Published November 1993**

**THE STORY:** When Jerry moves into his new house, he can't believe what he finds. Up in the dusty attic, hidden under an old quilt, is a shiny, black piano. As soon as he sees it, Jerry dreams about learning to play. But his dream quickly turns into a nightmare when he meets his new piano teacher — Dr. Shreek!

**THE STORY BEHIND THE STORY:** Inquiring *Goosebumps* fans want to know: Who is the ghost who plays the piano in Jerry's house? We don't know much, but we do know she was one of Dr. Shreek's unfortunate students. Her name was Mara Klane. And she lived in Jerry's house with her dog, Dino, a miniature greyhound.

Mara decided to take piano lessons because she was lonely and bored. Too bad for her—she was one of Dr. Shreek's most talented students. She had such *beautiful* hands . . . .

**TOTALLY AWESOME! The parts of the book you'll never forget:** *Goosebumps* fans may never forget the creepy Dr. Shreek chanting over and over again: "Remember the hands. They're alive. Let them breathe." Ewwww!

**FRIGHTENING FACT:** There's only one song mentioned by name in the entire book. It's a song Jerry's mom can play on the piano. To find out what it is, unscramble the letters below.

S  I  K  H  P  T  C  O  S  C

Answer on page 47.

**Collector's Cap #12**
**The Executioner — No More Mr. Nice Guy!**
**from**
**A NIGHT IN TERROR TOWER**

**Goosebumps #27**

**Published January 1995**

**THE STORY:** Sue and her brother Eddie are having a great time visiting London. Then they lose their tour group and find themselves locked inside a terrifying prison tower. That's bad. What's worse? They're being followed by an evil stranger cloaked in black . . . who wants them dead!

**THE STORY BEHIND THE STORY:** The Terror Tower is a lot like the Tower of London in England. That's because the idea for *A Night in Terror Tower* came to R.L. Stine when he was visiting the Tower of London. "I remember I walked up a very narrow stairway," R.L. said. "The stairs twisted around and around, and when I reached the top, I faced a solid wall. It was *really* creepy. That's what gave me the idea for Terror Tower."

**TOTALLY AWESOME! The parts of the book you'll never forget:** *Goosebumps* fans will never forget the most moving words in the book—the words that make Sue and Eddie go back in time. To find the words, cross out the letters that appear with the numbers 3 and 9 on a telephone.

D M O X F V A R D Y U M,

L W E O V F X A R I M S,

X Y M O V F D A R U W S.

Answer on page 47.

**Collector's Cap #13**
**The Horrors Welcome You**
**to the Scariest Rides!**
**from**
**ONE DAY AT HORRORLAND**

**Goosebumps #16**

**Published February 1994**

**THE STORY:** The Morris family is hopelessly lost. They're searching for Zoo Gardens Theme Park. But they're not having much luck. Then they stumble upon another amusement park. It's called HorrorLand, and it looks kind of cool. Until the Horrors show up — the creepy creatures who work at the park. And those rides. There's something deadly about those rides. Real deadly!

**THE STORY BEHIND THE STORY:** HorrorLand is run by strange monsters called Horrors. No one knows too much about them. Their story isn't told in *One Day at HorrorLand*. But they do have a history. The legend goes that fifty years ago, the Horrors were once normal people who worked at an old-time carnival. One terribly hot summer, the carnival visited a town in Ohio. And a horrible fire broke out.

The blaze spread quickly. There was no way anyone could have escaped or survived. But when the police searched the smoldering ashes, they discovered — nothing! Not a single trace of the carnival workers.

Rumor has it that those same carnival workers found their way to other employment . . . at HorrorLand. **TOTALLY AWESOME! The parts of the book you'll never forget:** True *Goosebumps* fans will never forget the ghastliest ride at HorrorLand: The Coffin Cruise — a relaxing Float to the Grave. Lizzy Morris lies down in a real coffin and begins to float downstream. A nice, relaxing ride, until . . . the coffin lid slams shut! Lizzy can't open the lid, no matter how hard she pushes. And the air inside the closed dark coffin grows hot. Hot and stale. It's hard to breathe . . . .

Are you a true *Goosebumps* fan? What happens next? **HAVE A GOOD SHRIEK!:** What can you order at the HorrorLand Hotel?

Unscramble the letters to find out!

OMOD  ERSIVEC

*Doom*

Answer on page 47.

**Collector's Cap #14**
**Cuddles — He's One Hungry Hamster!**
**from**
**MONSTER BLOOD II**

**Goosebumps** #18

**Published April 1994**

**THE STORY:** No one believes Evan's stories about Monster Blood. Then Evan and his friend, Andy, feed the green, quivering slime to Cuddles the class hamster. And Cuddles starts growing . . . and growing . . . and growing . . . !

**THE STORY BEHIND THE STORY:** Every kid who's read *Monster Blood II* wants to know more about Conan Barber. He's the bully in Evan's class who's better known as Conan the Barbarian. Conan acts tough, but he has a secret that can now be shared with true *Goosebumps* fans.

Conan sleeps with a teddy bear he calls Fluffster, and Conan's momsie tucks him in every night with a glass of cocoa and a bedtime story. All together now . . . Aaaw!

**FRIGHTENING FACTS:** Here are some facts by the numbers . . .

1) *Monster Blood II* was the first-ever sequel in *Goosebumps*. Since then there have been three other

sequels published. Can you name them?

2)The name Trigger (Evan's dog) appears 26 times in Chapter One of *Monster Blood II*. That could be a record for the most-mentioned name in a single chapter of a character that is *not* the main character. Can you find another?

**HAVE A GOOD SHRIEK!:** What time is it when a Monster Blood-eating hamster sits on your bed? Unscramble the words to find out!


NEW GET A TIME BED TO!


Answer on page 47.

**Collector's Cap #15**
**The Phantom Strikes!**
**from**
**THE PHANTOM OF THE AUDITORIUM**

**Goosebumps #24**

**Published October 1994**

**THE STORY:** Brooke and her best friend, Zeke, have won the lead roles in the school play, *The Phantom.* But someone is trying really hard to make sure the play never goes on! Could that someone be . . . the Phantom?

**THE STORY BEHIND THE STORY:** At the end of *The Phantom of the Auditorium,* we find out who the Phantom really is. But there are still a lot of questions left unanswered:

• What happened to him 72 years ago that turned him into a phantom?

• Who wrote the play about the Phantom?

• Has the Phantom been haunting Woods Mill Middle School all these years?

Not even R.L. Stine knows the answer to the first two questions. They remain a mystery — for now. But it is definitely true that Woods Mill Middle School *is* haunted. Just ask any kid who has eaten in the lunchroom!

**TOP SECRET! FOR GOOSEBUMPS FANS ONLY!:**
There's something only Brooke — and super *Goosebumps* fans like you — knows about Zeke. What are we talking about? Crack the numbers code below and you'll see.

|    |    | S |   |    |    |    |   |    |    | A | S |
|----|----|---|---|----|----|----|---|----|----|---|---|
| 19 | 22 | 8 | 7 | 18 | 15 | 15 |   | 4  | 22 | 26 | 9 | 8 |

|    |    |   |    |    |   |    | A  |    | A  |    | A  | S |
|----|----|---|----|----|---|----|----|----|----|----|----|---|
| 16 | 22 | 9 | 14 | 18 | 7 | 11 | 26 | 17 | 26 | 14 | 26 | 8 |

Answer on page 47.

## Collector's Cap #16
### Slappy — He Walks, He Stalks!
### from
### NIGHT OF THE LIVING DUMMY

**Goosebumps** #7

### Published May 1993

**THE STORY:** What a terrific find! Lindy Powell has uncovered a ventriloquist dummy. She names him Slappy and has a great time learning to make him talk. Then Lindy's sister, Kris, gets a dummy of her own. Mr. Wood. And that's when the fun stops — and the evil begins. Are the dummies behind it all? No way. Right? Hmmm . . .

**THE STORY BEHIND THE STORY:** Slappy is very proud of his family tree, but no one knows the real story of his creation. He claims he's related to the great redwoods, but that sounds like a really tall tale!

Here's what we do know . . . Slappy looks an awful lot like a dummy R.L. Stine had when he was a kid. R.L. Stine used to try to scare his brother with his dummy. Do you think the two dummies are related? It's possible.

**TOTALLY AWESOME!** The parts of the book you'll never forget: *The magic words that bring Mr. Wood to life:*

    *Karru marri odonna loma molonu karrano.*

*Mr. Wood's best lines:*
- "Is that a mustache, or are you eating a rat?"
- "Your face reminds me of a wart I had removed!"
- "If we count your chins, will it tell us your age?"

**TOP SECRET! FOR GOOSEBUMPS FANS ONLY!:** Slappy makes a comeback in *Night of the Living Dummy II.* But for really hot news, cross out every Z, A, and P below!

CZPOAMPAIZNG ASPOZOZN: ANPIAGPHZT OPFA

ZTPAZHZE AALPZIZVAIZAAPPNG DZUMPMZY IAAIAI.

Answer on page 47.

## PETRIFYING PUZZLES AND
## GRUESOME GAMES

So you think you're a *Goosebumps* fan? Maybe even the ULTIMATE *Goosebumps* fan? Well, here's your chance to show your stuff. These puzzles aren't for kids who've read one or two *Goosebumps* books. They're for the true collector — the kid who likes being scared, all the time, by the creepy creatures that haunt *Goosebumps*.

You can check your puzzle answers on pages 47–48 — if you dare!

Let the games begin!

## GOOSEBUMPS CAP SLAPPIN' GAME
### Warning: This game is for serious
### Goosebumps fans only.

Okay, you've been warned. If you still want to try your luck, here are the rules. You'll need two or more players for each game. (No fair using ghosts—you have to be able to see your opponent!)

1. Each player places an equal number of Collector's Caps face up in a single stack.

2. Flip the Curly slammer. Whoever gets the slammer to land Curly-side up, goes first.

3. The first player asks the second player a *Goosebumps* trivia question. Use the questions on the next page, or try one of your own. If the first player answers correctly, he or she gets to throw the Curly slammer down on the stack. He or she keeps any Caps that flip over.

4. Restack the remaining Caps. Now it's the second player's turn to ask the question. Keep playing

until every Collector's Cap in the pile has flipped over.

5. The player who flips over the most Caps wins the game.

## Questions:

1. Who is the director at Camp Nightmoon in *Welcome to Camp Nightmare*?

2. How many gold stars does it take to win a prize at the library in Timberland Falls in *The Girl Who Cried Monster*?

3. What is the name of Evan's great-aunt in *Monster Blood*?

4. What does Max find in his attic in *Let's Get Invisible!*?

5. While Hannah stays at home in *The Ghost Next Door*, where is her best friend, Janey?

6. What cereal is Skipper Matthews' favorite late-night snack in *Attack of the Mutant*?

7. What creepy, crawly creatures is Todd Barstow obsessed with in *Go Eat Worms!*?

8. Dr. Deep has only one rule for Billy and Sheena in *Deep Trouble* — stay away from what?

Answers on page 47.

# Hide and Go Scare!

## Top Secret! For GOOSEBUMPS Fans Only!

When it comes to *Goosebumps*, you never know what (or who) is hiding just around the bend. Hidden in this wordsearch are words from the titles of lots of *Goosebumps* books. First fill in the blanks. Next find the missing words in the wordsearch. Then, to learn the title of the July 1995 Goosebumps, unscramble the letters that you didn't circle in the word search.

Oh, one last rule. You can't look at your books to find the missing words. Real *Goosebumps* fans don't need to!

1. _____ Cheese and Die!

2. The _____ Next Door

3. Stay Out of the _____

4. Ghost _____

5. The _____ of Fever Swamp

6. _____ Lessons Can Be Murder!

7. Why I'm Afraid of _____

8. Let's _____ Invisible!

9. Welcome to _____ Nightmare

10. The Haunted _____

11. Be Careful What You _____ For

12. The Scarecrow_____ at Midnight

13. Go Eat _____!

14. It Came from Beneath the _____

15. The _____ of the Auditorium

16. You Can't _____ Me!

```
Y  J  P  I  A  N  O  L  M  F
A  W  A  L  K  S  R  R  A  L
S  O  T  S  H  E  M  C  S  O
H  R  S  C  E  J  A  I  K  W
C  M  O  A  C  M  N  S  I  E
A  S  H  R  P  K  E  S  H  R
E  O  G  E  A  E  H  T  A  E
B  A  M  T  B  O  R  P  Y  W
P  H  A  N  T  O  M  G  E  T
O  L  T  N  E  M  E  S  A  B
```

TITLE: _ _ _   _ _ _ _ _ _ _   _ _   _ _ _ _
_ _ _ _ _ _ _ _

Answers on page 47.

# The Word Is <u>Scared</u>

What's your favorite *Goosebumps* story? How about one you and your friends write yourselves?

Gather a bunch of *Goosebumps* fans in one room. Fill in all the blanks by asking for the kind of word written below the spaces. DO NOT read the story first! When you're finished filling in the blanks, read your terrifying tale out loud.

**IT GREW IN THE** _____!
Name of room in your house

**by**_____**and** _____
Names of two kids in your class

I remember when I first saw _____.
something in
your refrigerator

It was a dark and _____ _____.
kind of weather      a part of the day

My brothers and sisters were already tucked into

their _____. But not me. That's the time
thing in your room

I picked to go exploring in my parents'_____.
room in
your house

All I was looking for was a quick _____.
something you eat

But when I opened the door, my eyes met with a

horrible _____. It was _____ and _____
             thing              size           color

and had _____ _____s. I had never seen
        number  body part

anything so _____. I ran out the front door
              description

to my neighbor's _____. The scary thing followed
                    thing

me. And then it turned _____! So I kept on
                            color

_____ing. It wouldn't stop chasing me.
 action word

And the faster it ran, the _____er it got! Aah!
                              description

Look out! Here it comes now!

## Sorry, Right Number!

Don't pick up the phone! Some pretty scary *Goosebumps* questions are waiting for you on the other end! Do you dare answer them?

Each letter in the missing answer is represented by a number below. All you have to do is look at your telephone and find the letter that goes with the number. In case you haven't guessed yet, here's the tricky part: Each number on your phone appears with three letters! It's up to you to figure out which letter goes in the blank. We've done one for you!

P.S. Don't bother dialing *O* for operator assistance. No one can help you now!

Example:

What did Sabrina dress as for Halloween in *The Haunted Mask*?

```
C  A  T  W  O  M  A  N
2  2  8  9  6  6  2  6
```

1. What does the label say on the bottle of tanning lotion Larry finds in the trash in *My Hairiest Adventure*?

```
__ __ __ __ __ - __ __ __
 4  6  7  8  2    8  2  6
```

2. What is the name of the mummy hand that Gabe carries with him for luck in *The Curse of the Mummy's Tomb*?

```
__ __ __   __ __ __ __ __ __ __
 8  4  3    7  8  6  6  6  6  3  7
```

3. Where will you find the Doom Slide?

$\overline{\phantom{0}}\ \overline{\phantom{0}}\ \overline{\phantom{0}}\ \overline{\phantom{0}}\ \overline{\phantom{0}}\ \overline{\phantom{0}}\ \overline{\phantom{0}}\ \overline{\phantom{0}}\ \overline{\phantom{0}}\ \overline{\phantom{0}}$
4  6  7  7  6  7  5  2  6  3


4. What does Grandpa Kurt, in *The Scarecrow Walks at Midnight*, keep in his living room?

7  8  8  3  3  3  3    2  7  6  9  6    2  3  2  7


5. What birthday present did Michael's bratty little sister, Tara, ruin in *The Cuckoo Clock of Doom*?

2  4  2  9  2  5  3


6. What is Terri's spooky hobby in *Ghost Beach*?

4  7  2  8  3  7  8  6  6  3    7  8  2  2  4  6  4  7


Answers on page 48.

# Creepy, Crawly Crossword!

What's a three-letter word for a *Goosebumps* expert?
Y-O-U!

## ACROSS

1. Middle school where *The Phantom* is performed (2 words).
4. Dr. Brewer is in danger of becoming a house_____.
5. Name of the dummy found in the Dumpster in *Night of the Living Dummy*.
8. In *Be Careful What You Wish For*, Samantha plays _____ball.
9. Name of Lindy Powell's twin sister.
10. What does Grady name the stray dog he finds in *The Werewolf of Fever Swamp*?
11. What Dr. Shreek's students wish they had done before their next lesson.
13. The signs at HorrorLand: No _____.
14. What hairy creature does Eddie try to drop on Courtney's head in *You Can't Scare Me!*?

## DOWN

1. What creepy, crawly creatures are in Todd Barstow's spaghetti?
2. Skipper collects comics. His friend, Wilson, collects rubber_____.
3. Lucy is sure this person is a monster.
6. In *Monster Blood II*, Evan and Andy move to this city.
7. In *Night of the Living Dummy II*, Amy is practicing to be a _____.
12. Gary Lutz's bee-loving next-door neighbor is Mr._____.

Answer on page 48.

## Beware of Dogs (and Cats)!

Here's a game with some real bite!  Match the pet to the *Goosebumps* book it appears in.

1. Whitey      A. *Night of the Living Dummy*

2. Petey       B. *Be Careful What You Wish For . . .*

3. Rusty       C. *The Ghost Next Door*

4. Punkin     D. *Monster Blood*

5. Barky      E. *Welcome to Dead House*

6. Trigger    F. *Let's Get Invisible!*

Answers on page 48.

## ANSWERS

**Page   5:** THE MAGNIFICENT MOLECULE MAN

**Page   7:** HE WAS ALL TIED UP IN HIS WORK

**Page 13:** The real world isn't as scary as the monsters we can dream up.

**Page 15:** GROSS; WEIRD; COOL.

**Page 17:** HE GETS HIVES

**Page 19:** MAKE LIKE A TREE AND LEAVE!

**Page 23:** LEFTY

**Page 25:** CHOPSTICKS

**Page 27:** MOVARUM, LOVARIMS, MOVARUS

**Page 29:** DOOM SERVICE

**Page 31:** TIME TO GET A NEW BED!

**Page 33:** HE STILL WEARS KERMIT PAJAMAS

**Page 35:** COMING SOON: *NIGHT OF THE LIVING DUMMY III.*

**Page 37:** 1. Big Al; 2. six; 3. Kathryn; 4. a magic mirror; 5. at camp; 6. Frosted Flakes; 7. worms; 8. coral reefs.

**Pages 38–39:** 1. Say; 2. Ghost; 3. Basement; 4. Beach; 5. Werewolf; 6. Piano; 7. Bees; 8. Get; 9. Camp; 10. Mask; 11. Wish; 12. Walks; 13. Worms; 14. Sink; 15. Phantom; 16. Scare

THE HORROR AT CAMP JELLYJAM

**Pages 42–43:** 1. INSTA-TAN; 2. THE SUMMONER; 3. HORRORLAND; 4. STUFFED BROWN BEAR; 5. BICYCLE; 6. GRAVESTONE RUBBINGS

**Page 45:**

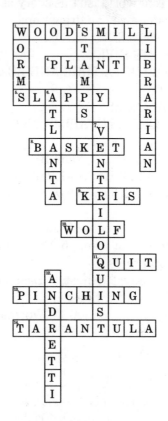